Measure, Pour & Mix Kitchen Science Tricks

James Lewis

Ⓜ Meadowbrook Press
Distributed by Simon & Schuster
New York

Library of Congress Cataloging-in-Publication Data
ISBN: 0-88166-134-1

Editor: Katherine Stevenson
Production Editor: Clara Jeffery
Production Manager: David Garbe
Designers: Kevin Bowen, Cathy Cullinane-Skraba
Illustrator: Steve McInturff

S&S Ordering #: 0-671-70701-9

Published by Meadowbrook Press, 18318 Minnetonka Boulevard, Deephaven, MN 55391.

BOOK TRADE DISTRIBUTION by Simon & Schuster, a division of Simon and Schuster, Inc., 1230 Avenue of the Americas, New York, NY 10020.

90 91 92 93 5 4 3 2 1

Printed in the United States of America

To my wife, Nancy
and my two children,
Tiffany and Jared

Contents

Preface

Children feel a special curiosity about the kitchen. To encourage this curiosity some parents involve their young children in setting the table or washing dishes, while others invite them to help prepare and cook food. Still others have their children help with shopping and putting away groceries. No matter what approach parents use, a child's desire to get involved in the kitchen is hard to subdue—some youngsters just can't wait to get their hands in the mixing bowl.

This book offers many suggestions for parents who want to involve their children in the kitchen in a fun and constructive way. The activities offer both parents and children an opportunity to work together at a time that's less busy than mealtime. They also show children how their parents use scientific concepts in the kitchen every day. And, most importantly, the activities provide new opportunities for parents to build special relationships with their children.

James Lewis

Acknowledgments

The development of this book can be credited to Bruce Lansky, publisher at Meadowbrook Press. Mr. Lansky's commitment to books that encourage parent-child involvement is commendable. Special thanks must be given to Mr. Lansky's staff, who have always been friendly, professional, supportive, and helpful. They have taken simple science concepts and made them come alive. Lisa Nyberg and Justin Field always assisted me when I needed help understanding science concepts. The Springfield Public Library and its staff were extremely helpful. Finally, I thank my family for allowing me the time to write and for sacrificing their needs to support mine.

J.L.

Making Kitchen Science Safe

Science in the kitchen can be wonderful fun, but make sure it's safe fun, too. Just follow these simple safety rules:

1. **Be present when your children attempt even the simplest of the activities in this book.** Supervise them very carefully during activities that use glass, knives, objects with points or sharp edges, small objects, or any ingredients that could be swallowed.

2. **Instruct your children always to ask permission before using any kitchen ingredients, utensils, or appliances.** All the items in the kitchen have specific uses, and your children should not think of them as toys.

3. **Plan ahead by first reading each activity completely,** then assembling all the supplies you need.

4. **Clean all materials thoroughly before using them in the activities.** Make sure you remove any residue inside plastic containers. Don't use containers that were used to hold medicines or cleansers. Make sure none of the containers have sharp edges.

5. **Teach your children never to put anything in their mouths unless you tell them it's OK.** Even "safe" chemicals such as vinegar and baking soda should be handled with care.

6. **Store all chemicals out of your children's reach.** Return all ingredients and utensils to their proper storage areas after each activity.

7. **Encourage your children to keep their clothes clean by wearing old shirts or aprons.** Food coloring can stain clothes. Dressing up makes science in the kitchen more fun, too!

8. **Show your children a safe way to reach the kitchen counter and sink,** two areas which are used in many of the activities.

9. **Remind your children to wash their hands before** and **after each activity** and anytime they get messy or dirty.

10. **To avoid burns use potholders when moving anything that might be hot.** Always test the temperature of the hot water from the kitchen faucet before your children use it.

11. **After each activity clean up the kitchen right away, with your children's help.** The kitchen should be clean and safe, with no slippery wet spots on the floor and no utensils left out to tempt your children into unsupervised experiments.

12. **Prepare for the unexpected.** Though these activities are planned with safety in mind, know what to do if an accident should occur—for example, if some ingredient splashes in your child's eye.

A Note to Parents

1. Most of the activities in this book have been selected because they show a scientific process your children can actually **see** and, therefore, understand. As the parent, **you're** best qualified to decide which activities your children will understand and enjoy.

2. Though the activities in this book are designed for children in kindergarten through third grade, older children might enjoy them, too. In fact, older children might understand the science principles behind the activities in more detail.

3. The procedures given for each activity are only suggestions; feel free to modify them. You might wish to read the directions first and then rephrase them for your children.

4. Most of the activities are designed to take only about five minutes each, but some take up to a week to see the results. Encourage your children to be patient and try other activities while they're waiting.

5. Encourage your children to repeat an activity if they want to. One brief exposure to a new idea might not satisfy their curiosity.

6. Encourage your children to try variations of each activity—for example, longer times or different ingredients—to expand their understanding of the concept presented. Just make sure you supervise the variations to keep them safe.

7. Always encourage your children to explain what happens in each activity, but don't demand answers or turn the activities into drills. Let your children **enjoy** them! Motivating your children to explain things in their own words will foster their understanding. You can help by paraphrasing their responses and showing them how to use new words and concepts.

8. The materials you'll need are listed on the page for each activity and in a master list at the beginning of the book. You'll find most of these materials already in your kitchen, but some (marked with asterisks) might require a quick trip to the store.

Materials

Kitchen Supplies:

Aluminum soft drink cans
(empty)
Bowls and plates (plastic)
Coffee mugs (plastic)
Cookie cutters
Cookie sheet
Cooling rack
Drinking glasses (plastic and
glass)
Forks, spoons, and knives
(plastic)
Ice cream container (round)
Jars, plastic (quart, pint, and
baby food, with lids)
Liquid soap or dish detergent
Measuring cups and spoons
Muffin tin
Pans
Paper cups
Paper towels
Pie tin
Plastic bags (sandwich and
bread or vegetable)
Plastic wrap (clear)
Rolling pin
Sharp knife
Soft drink bottles
(clear plastic)
Soup or juice can (empty)
Straws (plastic)
Table knife
Toothpicks

Kitchen Ingredients:

Baking soda
Cooking oil
Cornstarch
Flour
Food coloring
Ice cubes
*Rock salt
Salt
Vinegar

Household Supplies:

Index cards (3-inch by 5-inch)
*Cheesecloth
Cloth (small pieces)
*Cork (to fit in a pop bottle)
*Cotton string
*Eyedropper (optional)
*Funnel (small)
*Magnifying glass (optional)
Marbles
Marking pen
Masking tape
Needle
*Paper clips
Pencils
Pennies
*Plastic tape (electrical tape)
Pocket mirror
Popsicle sticks (optional)
Rubber bands
Ruler
Scissors
*Wire screen
Writing paper

Foods:

Bread
Butter or margarine
Celery
Coffee grounds or tea leaves
*Dried beans (pinto, black-eyed,
lima, kidney, or red)
Eggs (raw and hard-boiled)
Fruit juice (orange, grape, etc.)
Milk
Potatoes
*Sprouting seeds (alfalfa,
red clover, mung bean,
soybean, wheat berry, radish,
and/or sunflower)
Tomato soup
*Whipping cream

***Items that might require a
quick trip to the store.**

Basic
Activities

What's in There?

Can you guess if this bottle is empty or full?

Parent's Note:

Often, parents can excite children's curiosity by offering a challenge like . . . "That empty pop bottle isn't really empty, and I'll *prove* it." With a little coaxing, the children will think up new ways to prove it, too. In this activity children will learn that kitchen air is everywhere—even inside an empty pop bottle.

What You Need:

An empty, clear plastic soft drink bottle; a small piece of paper.

What To Do:

1. Place an empty bottle on its side on the kitchen counter. Put the bottle opening even with the edge of the counter.

2. Next, make a tiny paper ball. It should be much smaller than the hole in the bottle—about the size of a pea.

3. Carefully place the paper ball just inside the mouth of the bottle, but don't let it fall into the bottle! (You might want to hold the bottle to keep it from rolling.)

4. Now try to blow the paper ball into the bottle. Try blowing gently or hard, whichever way you want. Whoops! What happens?

What Did You See?

No matter whether you blew gently or hard, the paper ball always popped out of the bottle.

Why Did It Happen?

The bottle might *look* empty, but there's actually something inside it—AIR! Blowing into the bottle pushes more air inside, but since the bottle is already full, some of the air has to come back out. And the air coming out pops the paper ball back out, too.

Bag It

Do you think it would be hard to arm wrestle air?

Parent's Note:

You can help your children learn more about air and air pressure just by using plastic bags from the kitchen. These bags will help your children remember that air not only takes up space, but it's also very strong.

What You Need:

Plastic sandwich bags; rubber bands; plastic tape; a large plastic jar or container (with an opening 3 to 4 inches in diameter—or 7 to 9 centimeters).

What To Do:

1. Take a plastic bag, blow some air into it, and put it over the mouth of a large jar.

2. Make sure there's enough air in the bag to make the bag stick up above the jar. Now fasten the bag onto the jar with a rubber band and some plastic tape. Make it airtight!

3. Do you think you can push the bag down into the jar? Try it! Push gently, though, so you don't break the bag.

4. Now try unsealing the bag, holding it so it's drooping down inside the mouth of the jar, and then sealing it again. Try pulling the bag out of the jar. What happens?

What Did You See?

You just couldn't push the bag into the jar or pull the bag out, no matter how much you tried!

Why Did It Happen?

Air takes up space just like water does. The air that is trapped inside the bag and the jar will stay there unless there is a hole through which it can escape. Pushing the air trapped inside the bag reduces the air space inside the bag and the jar and so increases the pressure. The bag will move a little, but the harder you push down, the more pressure builds up and pushes back. When you try to pull the bag, the air space increases, reducing the pressure inside the jar; however, the outside air then has an equal amount of pressure and keeps the bag inside. If you poke a hole through the bag you can easily push or pull the bag.

Pick Me Up

Can you lift an empty pop bottle using just a straw?

Parent's Note:

This activity uses straws to introduce the principle of leverage. You can put a little water in the plastic bottle to make the activity more of a challenge, but make sure your child experiments over the sink! You might try finding additional ways to lift the bottle—have fun with it!

What You Need:

An empty, plastic soft drink bottle; several plastic straws (just in case some get weakened or bent).

What To Do:

1. Try lifting a soft drink bottle with a straw. First, let's try laying the bottle on its side and balancing it on the straw. Any luck?

2. Now try sticking the straw in the top of the bottle and lifting. Does that work? How about looping the straw around the top and lifting? That just *might* work, but let's try just one more way . . .

3. Bend the straw about 2 to 3 inches (or 5 to 7 centimeters) from the end and push the bent end a little way into the bottle.

4. Now pull the straw upward until the tip is against one side of the bottle and the bent part is against the opposite side. Now lift carefully. You've got it!

What Did You See?

You could lift the bottle only by bending the straw and poking the bent part in the bottle—that's the only way you could get a good enough grip to lift the bottle.

Why Did It Happen?

When you bend the straw, it tries to straighten itself back into its natural shape. But when you poke the bent part into the mouth of the bottle, it doesn't have enough room to straighten itself out. Instead, it gets stuck in the mouth of the bottle—so stuck that you can use it to lift up the bottle!

The Last Straw

How long is the longest straw you can drink through?

Parent's Note:

Drinking with straws is more common at fast food restaurants than at home, but have your children try this activity at home, where you can closely supervise. By creating a vacuum in a long tube made of straws taped together, children will learn about the power of air pressure.

What You Need:

10 to 15 straight plastic straws; plastic tape; scissors; a clear plastic quart bottle or jar.

What To Do:

1. Let's practice drinking through a straw. Fill this bottle with water and use the straw to drink just a little. That's easy.

2. Do you think that you could drink just as easily through 2 straws? Use this tape to connect 2 straws and try drinking through them now. Any difference?

3. Now that you've mastered that, try drinking through 3 straws taped together. Any trouble? You might need to put the bottle on the floor.

4. Keep taping straws together until they're as high as you can reach. Can you still get the water all the way up to your mouth? What makes the water go that high?

What Did You See?

It's easy to drink from just a single straw—the water comes right up when you start to suck. But when you taped many straws together, you had to suck very hard to get the water all the way to the top.

Why Did It Happen?

Air pushes on everything with a lot of force. Air pushes on both the water in the straws and the water in the bottle. But sucking the air out of the straws and into your lungs means that no air is left in the straws to push down on the water—the only air left is the air pushing on the water in the bottle. So the air in the bottle pushes the water in the bottle down, and the water goes up the straws. It's possible that the air could push the water about 34 feet up the straws. Wow!

Temp Test

Is the water hot or cold? Are you sure?

Parent's Note:

The sense of touch is an important sense, but one that can't always be trusted. In this activity children will decide whether water is hot or cold. Try this activity yourself, then supervise your child *closely* to make sure the hot water is not too hot! And the cold water should *not* be so cold it makes your child's hand ache.

What You Need:

3 medium-sized plastic bowls (large enough for your child's hands).

What To Do:

1. Take a bowl and fill it with very cold water and set it in the sink or on the kitchen counter. Then fill another bowl with *very warm* water—not too hot! You don't want to burn yourself. Set it beside the other bowl.

2. Now fill the last bowl with water that doesn't feel either cool or warm—in fact, if it's the right temperature, you'll hardly be able to feel it at all!

3. Roll up your sleeves and put one hand in the very cold water and the other hand in the very warm water. Leave your hands in the bowls for quite a while (count with Mom or Dad up to 3 or 5 minutes).

4. Now take your hands out of the 2 bowls and then put them both in the middle bowl. Does the water in the middle bowl feel cold? hot? or both?!

What Did You See?

The water in the middle bowl felt both hot and cold! It felt cold to the hand that had been in the very warm water and felt hot to the hand that had been in the cold water. It was hard to decide if the water in the middle bowl was actually cold or hot.

Why Did It Happen?

Your body's ability to tell hot from cold depends on what you were touching last. For example, if you wash your hands after you have been playing with snow or ice, warm tap water feels very hot, and even cold water feels warm!

The Big Freeze

Does water get bigger or smaller when it freezes?

Parent's Note:

Children know about ice cubes and Popsicles and perhaps about icicles and frozen lakes outside in the winter. But they might not have thought about the relationship of ice to water. This activity will show children that freezing temperatures cause water to freeze and expand. If you have a freezer with an automatic defrost, cover the glasses with plastic wrap so the ice in the glass doesn't wear away.

What You Need:

A clear plastic glass with sloping sides; a marking pen or masking tape.

What To Do:

1. First, take a plastic glass, fill it half full of water, and set it on a flat countertop or table. Make a mark (or put some tape) on the glass at the water level. Be very careful to mark the *exact* level of the water in the glass.

2. Now set the glass on a flat, level spot in the freezer and leave it overnight. You know the water will freeze like an ice cube, but will the ice be below the line? on the line? or above the line?

3. The next day, remove the glass from the freezer and look at the line. How high is the ice? Why is it higher than the mark?

4. Allow the ice to melt in the glass and see whether it goes back down to the line.

What Did You See?

The water in the glass turned to ice when it froze. The ice level was above the water mark; the water got *bigger* when it froze.

Why Did It Happen?

Many things, like metal, get smaller in cold temperatures. But water is different—it actually gets bigger when it freezes! When water freezes, the tiny particles of water move away from each other and become bigger solid crystals. You've seen this happen when tiny raindrops freeze to become big fluffy snowflakes. In ice, these crystals join together to form a rigid pattern that takes up more space than the little particles of water. That's why car radiators have special antifreeze in them instead of plain water, and why water pipes sometimes leak in the winter if the water inside them freezes.

Popsicle Race

Which freezes faster—juice or water?

Parent's Note:

In this activity children will compare the freezing times of plain water and fruit juices. You'll need to help them keep track of the time so they can check the liquids in the freezer at regular intervals. And everyone will be able to eat the fruit Popsicles after they've frozen, so pick your favorite flavor of juice and join the experiment!

What You Need:

Fruit juice (orange juice works well because it has pulp in it); plastic spoons or wooden Popsicle sticks; a plate; 3 small plastic glasses, all the same size; water (about the same temperature as the juice).

What To Do:

1. Start by pouring juice into a small glass. If you have another kind of juice, pour it into a second glass.

2. Next, fill another glass with plain tap water. Make sure you fill all glasses to the same level. Let all the liquids reach room temperature by leaving them out for a half hour.

3. Place a stick or spoon in each of the glasses, put the glasses on a plate, and put the plate with the glasses in the freezer.

4. Which Popsicle will freeze the fastest? Check the glasses every half hour. The differences in the liquids should be clear in 90 minutes, and they should all be completely frozen in 3 to 6 hours. Have fun eating your experiment when you're done, too!

What Did You See?

Plain water froze faster than fruit juice.

Why Did It Happen?

Juices are a mixture of water and tiny pieces of fruit. These fruit pieces keep the water droplets from turning to ice as quickly as plain water. Ice cream also freezes more slowly than water because of all the sugar, butterfat, and other goodies in it.

Double Vision

How do you look to a fish underwater?

Parent's Note:

Your children have probably never experienced swimming underwater and looking up at the surface to see how it reflects light—maybe you haven't, either! This activity shows children that water can reflect light just as a mirror does. A small pocket mirror will let children see the underside of the water's surface.

What You Need:

The kitchen sink or a plastic washtub or basin; a pocket mirror about 2 inches by 3 inches (5 centimeters by 8 centimeters) in size; plastic or masking tape.

What To Do:

1. First, tape a mirror onto the sink or basin so that it slopes (45-degree angle). Next, fill the sink with water so the top of the mirror is well covered.

2. Let the water settle so there are no more ripples. Can you see yourself in the *water*? Can you see yourself in the *mirror*?

3. Now stick 1 finger—*just* the finger—under the water and look at its reflection in the mirror. Does it look like your finger has grown another finger? If not, pull your finger away from the mirror a little. It's like seeing double!

4. Try turning your finger sideways and wiggling it. It looks like you're clapping with just 1 finger!

What Did You See?

The mirror reflected your finger, but so did the water's surface, so it looked like you had 2 fingers growing together! Neither the mirror nor the water reflected any other part of your hand, just the finger that was underwater.

Why Did It Happen?

The top surface of the water reflects light, but so does the *underside* of the surface. Your eye sees both reflections, the one in the mirror and the one made by the underside of the surface. The mirror lets you look at the underside of the water's surface, just like swimming underwater and looking up. Like a fish, you only see what's below the surface, not what's above it.

Disappearing Act

Can you make your favorite sticker disappear?

Parent's Note:

The now-you-see-it-now-you-don't qualities of this activity will peak children's curiosity. Water has a way of bending light which passes through it; in this case, it bends the light so that the sticker under the glass can't be seen from the side.

What You Need:

A clear plastic glass or jar (a container that has a flat bottom and straight, not beveled, sides works best); a sticker or postage stamp.

What To Do:

1. It's easy enough to see something when you drop it into a clear glass—you just look and there it is! Try putting your favorite sticker or a stamp *under* an empty glass. Can you still see it through the top of the glass?

2. Do you think you can still see the sticker if you look through the side of the glass? Take a look.

3. What would happen if you poured some water in the glass and looked down from the top. Can you still see the sticker?

4. Now look through the side of the full glass. Can you see the sticker that way?

What Did You See?

When the glass was empty, you could see the sticker from the top and through the side of the glass. When the glass was filled with water, you could see the sticker from above but not from the side—as though it had disappeared!

Why Did It Happen?

When the glass is empty, you can see the sticker because light hits it, bounces off, and goes straight to your eye, no matter whether you look from the top or through the side. When the glass is filled with water, however, the water causes some changes. If you look from above, the light still bounces straight back from the picture to your eye. But if you look from the side, the water *bends* the light so that it bounces off the side of the glass instead.

Candy-Colored Celery

Can you make celery turn different colors?

Parent's Note:

Many children can't believe that water travels from the roots of a tree to leaves 100 feet above. This activity uses celery to show how the process works—though on a smaller scale! A celery stalk with leaves on the top will make the demonstration very realistic.

What You Need:

A celery stalk (with leaves); 2 plastic glasses (straight vertical sides work best); a ½-teaspoon (2.5-milliliter) measure; a ¼-cup (60-milliliter) measure; a knife; red and blue food coloring.

What To Do:

1. Let's start by putting ¼ cup (or 60 milliliters) of water in each of 2 glasses. Now add ½ teaspoon (or 2.5 milliters) of red food coloring to one glass, and the same amount of blue to the other.

2. Next, have Mom or Dad split the stalk of celery with a knife. Place one of the split ends in the red water and the other in the blue.

3. Let the celery stand for several hours. You can check on it whenever you want. Can you guess what's happening?

4. Celery is supposed to be green! What color is it now? Cut the celery stalk and look at the tubes. What color are they?

What Did You See?

One side of the celery turned blue and the other side turned red. The tubes inside the celery were also colored.

Why Did It Happen?

Water droplets are attracted to the sides of the tubes in the celery stalk, so the water tends to pull itself upward along the narrow tubes. This tendency of water to creep through narrow tubes is called *capillary action*. The narrower the tube, the higher the water will rise— even as high as the top of a tree! Some tubes in the stems of plants are too small to see without a magnifying glass or microscope, but they make sure that water gets to every leaf on every plant so the plants can grow and stay green.

Super Beans

Can you make an ordinary cooking bean jump?

Parent's Note:

This activity will show children the immense power packed inside a little seed. A seed soaked in water for just a few hours expands slowly, but with tremendous force. You can also have your children try this activity by soaking beans in an old plastic container with a locking lid—the beans will actually break the sides of the container!

What You Need:

2 plastic glasses (1 large, 1 small); a metal lid from a saucepan; dried beans (pinto, black-eyed, lima, kidney, or red).

What To Do:

1. First, place a saucepan lid upside down on top of a large glass.

2. Now set a small plastic glass in the center of the lid and fill the glass to the brim with dried beans.

3. Next, add water to the glass of beans. The water should fill the glass to the brim.

4. Now just let the beans sit in the water for an hour and then check them. What happened?

What Did You See?

The beans became larger when soaked in water. As they grew bigger, they pushed upward in the glass until some beans spilled over the side of the glass and dropped into the metal lid.

Why Did It Happen?

Like other dried seeds, beans get bigger when placed in water because water seeps through the walls of the seed. As they swell, seeds push out with great force. A seed planted in dirt absorbs water from the dirt, starts to swell, and then pushes the dirt out of the way to make room for the new plant that will come from the seed.

Play It Again

Can you play water glasses like a musical instrument?

Parent's Note:

Children will love to create their own musical instruments and play with them. This activity combines kitchen science and music for lots of fun. Creating these glass chimes might inspire you and your children to experiment with other kitchen "instruments."

What You Need:

Any number of glasses (preferably of the same size—8 would be perfect); a teaspoon; an eyedropper (optional); small pieces of paper; a pencil.

What To Do:

1. First, let's take a glass and put some water in it—it doesn't matter how much.

2. Now tap the glass very gently with a teaspoon and listen to the sound. What do you think would happen to the sound if there was more or less water in the glass?

3. Experiment by emptying the glass and then tapping it as Mom or Dad gradually fills it from the bottom to the top. What happens?

4. Make a row of glasses with different levels of water in them. Can you arrange them from the highest note to the lowest? You might even want to play a song on them! Number the glasses and write down the numbers in the order for your song.

What Did You See?

When you tapped the glass it made a sound. A glass with lots of water made a low sound, and a glass with a little water made a high sound. The sounds made by a glass that was gradually filled up started out high and got lower and lower.

Why Did It Happen?

When you tap on something it makes a sound because it vibrates, or moves, stirring the air around it into sound waves. Things that are big, heavy, or thick vibrate more slowly than things that are small, light, or thin, so they make a lower sound—that's why big bass drums and tubas make lower sounds than little drums and whistles. Putting more water in a glass makes it vibrate more slowly, so it makes a lower sound.

Intermediate Activities

Weight Lifter

Can you lift a heavy container by blowing air?

Parent's Note:

This activity will show your children just how powerful air and air pressure really are. They'll be able to lift a heavy object using nothing more than air and a bag to hold it in! Be prepared for the container to tip over, too—make sure it has a watertight lid.

What You Will Need:

A strong, clear plastic bag with no holes (a sandwich, bread, or vegetable bag); a rubber band; plastic tape; a straw; scissors (optional); a large plastic container with a tight-fitting lid.

What To Do:

1. First, fill the container with water and put the lid on. Can you lift it and put it on the counter? You might need Mom or Dad's help.

2. Now wrap the open end of a plastic bag around the end of the straw. Wind a rubber band and plastic tape around the mouth of the bag so that it is firmly attached to the straw.

3. Let Mom or Dad lift the container so you can place the bag under it. Let the straw hang over the edge of the counter.

4. Now use the straw to slowly blow some air into the bag. What happens? Wow! Air is very strong.

What Did You See?

When you blew air into the bag, the bag got bigger and the air in it pushed the heavy container up and over.

Why Did It Happen?

Air takes up space, so when you blow air into a bag, the bag gets bigger and pushes anything on top of it out of the way. The power of air in containers is used in the brakes that stop trucks and buses and in machines that have to lift heavy loads. If you had enough strong plastic bags under your kitchen refrigerator and enough people blowing air into them, you could even use air to lift the refrigerator!

Rainbow Magic

Can you make many colors from just a few?

Parent's Note:

The baking cabinet is filled with things that can make wonderful cakes, cupcakes, muffins, and other treats. And nothing does more to dress up those treats for special occasions than food coloring! Your children will have lots of fun using basic colors to create lots of colors. You might want to do this activity in a place where spills won't matter, or protect your work area with newspapers.

What You Need:

A muffin tin (a white Styrofoam egg carton or small glasses, cups, or bowls also work well); 3 plastic bowls; blue, red, and yellow food coloring; 3 eye-droppers (straws will work as droppers, too).

What To Do:

1. Let's start by pouring clear tap water into all the round holes in the muffin tin. Fill the 3 bowls with just a little water, too.

2. Put a few drops of blue color in the first bowl, a few drops of red in the second bowl, and a few drops of yellow in the third.

3. Using the eyedroppers, try mixing 1 drop of blue water and 3 drops of yellow in one of the muffin tin holes. What color do they make?

4. Try mixing red with yellow, and then try blue and red. Keep making other colors by mixing red, blue, and yellow. Have fun! If you run out of room in the muffin tin, just empty it out and add clear water.

What Did You See?

You could use different combinations of the 3 basic colors to make all the colors of the rainbow.

Why Did It Happen?

The colors blue, red, and yellow are called the primary colors, which means that they come first. All other colors are made by mixing these primary colors together.

Dirt Buster

Can you clean clothes without a washing machine?

Parent's Note:

In this activity children will learn how soap helps to clean dishes, clothes, and bodies. Though your children might wash dishes, take baths, and help put dirty clothes in the washing machine, they might not have noticed how soap removes dirt, oil, and grease.

What You Need:

2 plastic glasses; 2 teaspoons; a table knife; butter or margarine; 2 small pieces of cloth, about 3 inches (or 8 centimeters) square; liquid soap or dish detergent.

What To Do:

1. Take 2 pieces of cloth and spread some butter or margarine on both of them. Let's pretend these pieces of cloth are your clothes and you've spilled butter or grease all over them.

2. Now fill a glass with very warm water and another with cold water. Put a piece of buttered cloth in each glass and hold it underwater with a spoon. What happens?

3. Finally, put 3 drops of liquid soap in each container and watch what happens when the soap hits the water.

4. After a while, slowly stir the water and soap in each glass. Use the spoons to take the cloth out of each glass and look for the butter. What happened to it?

What Did You See?

The hot water removed much of the butter—even more when you added some soap, which seemed to "grab" the butter and pull it to the top of the water. The cold water did not remove much butter from the cloth, even after you added soap.

Why Did It Happen?

Hot water melts butter and turns it into oil. Soap mixes with the oil and breaks large oil drops into tiny drops that float around in the soapy water. Cold water doesn't clean the butter off as well because it doesn't melt it first, and the soap can't break down the solid lump of butter. When your clothes get dirty, the dirt sticks to them because it has grease or oil in it. Water rinses away both the oil (which is attached to the soap) and the tiny pieces of dirt.

Green Slime

Would you like to make some fun, gooey slime?

Parent's Note:

Cornstarch, a baking ingredient almost as common as flour, makes foods thicker and more solid. In this activity cornstarch, combined with water, will show children a perfect example of a suspension—a mixture in which the particles of cornstarch do not dissolve, they just float in the water.

What You Need:

A plastic bowl or mug; a spoon; a fork; cornstarch; a tablespoon; green food coloring.

What To Do:

1. Start by measuring 5 tablespoons of cornstarch into a bowl. Then add 3 tablespoons of water combined with a drop of green food coloring.

2. Stir all the ingredients with a fork. The mixture might be difficult to stir—it should be like a thick liquid paste, not dry, solid, or runny.

3. When you have mixed the ingredients, try picking up a spoonful. What happens? Why won't the "slime" stay in the spoon?

4. Place the bowl of "slime" in the kitchen sink and have Mom or Dad spoon some into your cupped hands. Try squeezing it into a ball or rolling it between your hands. What happens when you stop squeezing it? Remember, a little water from the kitchen faucet will wash the "slime" away.

What Did You See?

The water and cornstarch made a sticky substance. The mixture acted like both runny water and solid modeling clay.

Why Did It Happen?

The cornstarch particles didn't dissolve in water; they just floated around suspended in the water, so the mixture is called a *suspension*. When you squeezed the slime or pushed a spoon into it, you forced some of the water out and made it more solid. But then when you let go, the water ran back in and it got slimy again. Yuck!

Butter Churn

Can you turn cream into butter?

Parent's Note:

In this activity your children will change cream, a liquid, into butter, a solid, in just a few short minutes. They'll be excited about making real homemade butter! Chilling the marbles and the glass container will make the butter form faster.

What You Need:

Whipping cream; a small glass container with a tight-fitting lid; 2 clean marbles; a plastic drinking glass; a plate; a knife; crackers.

What To Do:

1. Start by pouring whipping cream into a jar so it is half full. Then add 2 clean marbles to the jar and screw the lid on tightly. Why do you think you need to add the marbles?

2. Now shake the jar gently and listen to the marbles. Are they stirring the cream? Shake the jar until you cannot hear the marbles hitting the jar and the cream has separated into a milky liquid and a creamy solid.

3. Nice and quiet? Good! Carefully remove the lid and pour off the liquid into a glass. Dump what is left onto a plate.

4. Remove the marbles. Taste what's on the plate. Is it butter? Use the knife to spread some on a cracker. Put the leftover butter in the refrigerator and use it later.

What Did You See?

Shaking the whipping cream in the jar with the marbles turned it into butter and a drinkable liquid like milk.

Why Did It Happen?

Whipping cream (a liquid) turns into butter (a solid) when you shake and stir it. The marbles hit the fat droplets in the cream and force them to separate from the water. The fat droplets then join together to make a larger lump of fat called butter.

Stick Together

Can you pick up one ice cube with another ice cube?

Parent's Note:

The freezer is a useful tool for science in the kitchen, but many activities that make use of it take a long time to yield results. This activity, though, yields instant results because all you need is ice cubes and salt. Your children will learn that heat isn't the *only* thing that will melt ice!

What You Need:

Ice cubes; salt; a plastic glass; a short piece of string; a plastic dish; gloves.

What To Do:

1. First, put on a pair of gloves to keep your fingers warm. Now take 2 ice cubes and put them in a dish on the kitchen counter. Sprinkle some salt on one side of an ice cube.

2. Push the salted side of the cube against the other ice cube and hold it there while you count to 40. Let go slowly. Now lift a cube. What happens? Try sticking 3 or 4 ice cubes together like this.

3. Here's another trick. Float an ice cube in a glass that's brimming full with water. Now lay a wet string across the top of the ice cube and sprinkle salt on the string and ice cube.

4. Leave the string there until you count to 40. Now pull on the string. What happens?

What Did You See?

The salt made the ice cubes stick together. Salt also made the string stick to the ice cube floating in the glass of water.

Why Did It Happen?

Salt melts ice into water. When you sprinkled salt on a cube and held it against another cube, the salt melted part of both cubes. The water from the melted ice washed away the salt and then froze again. You were holding both cubes together so they froze together. The melted ice from the cube in the glass froze again around the string so the string stuck to the cube. Salt also melts ice on roads and sidewalks in cold winter weather.

Feels Frosty Outside

Do you know what makes dew? or frost?

Parent's Note:

This activity will show children how dew forms—and all they'll need to do it is a few ice cubes from the freezer. With the addition of another ingredient, salt, they'll even be able to make their own frost!

What You Need:

A medium-sized jar with a tight-fitting lid; a metal can (a clean soup can with NO sharp edges and the label removed); ice cubes; rock salt (or table salt); a paper towel.

What To Do:

1. First, fill a jar with ice and put the lid on tightly. Make sure the jar is very dry on the outside.

2. Place the jar on the counter and wait to see what happens. What do you see? Tiny water drops, just like dew, on the outside of the jar! The water couldn't have come from inside the jar because the lid is on. So where did it come from?

3. Next, take an empty soup can and fill it by putting in a layer of salt, a layer of ice chips and so on till you reach the top. As the ice melts, pour off any water and add more ice and salt. You might have to wait longer than before for this part of the experiment—take a break!

4. When you come back, what do you see on the outside of the can? Frost! It even *feels* cold! Try scraping some off with your fingernail.

What Did You See?

When you put ice in the jar, the jar got lots of little water droplets all over the outside—just like a cold glass of lemonade does in the summertime. When you put ice and salt in the can, the can got frost all over the outside.

Why Did It Happen?

Air has water in it, but the water droplets are too small to see. When warm air touches something cold like glass, the water in the air changes into bigger drops that we can see. In the same way, warm air outdoors floats up until it touches cold air high in the sky. Then the water droplets in the warm air turn to big drops called rain. Metal gets cold faster than glass. Adding salt to the ice makes the can become cold even faster, causing the water droplets that form on the outside of the can to refreeze into frost.

Bigger Than Life

Do things look bigger through water and plastic wrap?

Parent's Note:

Kids love to use a magnifying glass to look at small things—a bug, for example, or a sliver in their finger. In this activity your child will learn to *make* a magnifying glass using just tap water and some simple kitchen items.

What You Need:

Clear plastic wrap; rubber bands (or string or plastic tape); a round plastic tub (a 2-quart or 2.2-liter ice cream container, an oatmeal container, or an old plastic bowl); a coin; a table knife (optional); scissors or a knife (handle with care!); a salad plate.

What To Do:

1. Take an empty plastic container and let Mom or Dad cut a hole in the side. Make the hole big enough to put your hand—or at least a table knife—inside the container.

2. Now let's put clear plastic wrap *loosely* across the top of the container and fasten the edges with a rubber band. (You can use string or tape instead of the rubber band.)

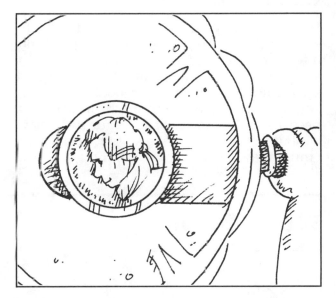

3. Next, pour some water on top of the plastic wrap. You might want to set the container in the sink or on the kitchen counter to make it level.

4. Put a coin on your finger and hold it outside the container, next to the hole. See how big it is? Now hold the coin inside the container and look down through the water. Does the water make the coin look bigger? Try holding some other things underneath it.

What Did You See?

The water in the plastic wrap acted like a magnifying glass or lens and made the things you held underneath it look bigger.

Why Did It Happen?

The plastic wrap held the water in a curved shape, like a curved glass lens, that bends light and makes the coin look larger than it is. Scientists use curved lenses made of glass to make tiny objects big enough to see.

Garden in a Jar

Can you grow food without dirt or sunlight?

Parent's Note:

In this activity children will learn how to grow edible sprouts in the kitchen. That might be a marvel to children who have not seen how seeds really grow! If you can't find seeds for sprouting at your local supermarket, try a food co-op. Your children will only need a small quantity of seeds for this activity, but fresh sprouts are so tasty that your family may want to grow them regularly.

What You Need:

Several 1-quart (or 1-liter), clear plastic jars; cheesecloth; rubber bands; a small metal cooling rack; a tray or pan big enough to hold the cooling rack; paper; masking tape; a pencil or pen; a tablespoon; sprouting seeds (alfalfa, soybean, red clover, wheat berry, mung bean, radish, or sunflower).

What To Do:

1. Place a tablespoon of each kind of seed in separate jars and ask Mom or Dad to help label each jar.

2. Next, stretch cheesecloth across the top of each jar and fasten it with a rubber band. Fill each jar with lukewarm water and let the seeds soak overnight.

3. The next day, drain the jars. Put a cooling rack in a tray or pan, then set the jars of wet seeds upside down on the rack so any water will drain out (the seeds will rot in standing water). Store the rack with the seeds in a cool, dry place, like the cupboard under the sink.

4. Make sure you rinse the seeds with slightly warm water twice a day—you might want to put a sign above the kitchen sink to remind you. When the seeds have grown into nice sprouts, expose them to the light until they turn green. Then rinse and taste!

What Did You See?

The seeds grew into sprouts, which are very young plants. Different seeds made different-shaped sprouts. You could eat the sprouts like lettuce, but the radish sprouts were very hot!

Why Did It Happen?

Plants grow from seeds. Seeds sprout best in dark, damp places. They don't need dirt or sunlight to start growing, but they *do* need a little water. Sprouts are a healthy food to eat. They taste great on salads and sandwiches, and mung bean sprouts are delicious cooked in Chinese dishes like chow mein.

Microfarming

Can you grow tiny plants on food?

Parent's Note:

This time your children will be growing plants that don't resemble plants—molds! These molds are *not* edible, but they are fascinating because of their different colors and textures. Let your children examine these plants with a magnifying glass and encourage them to be patient during the long growing process—the results are worth the wait.

What You Need:

2 small, clear plastic glasses; a pie tin; plastic wrap; rubber bands; paper towels; tomato soup; bread; plastic tape; a magnifying glass.

What To Do:

1. Let's start by putting a wet paper towel in the bottom of a pie tin and then putting a piece of bread on top of the towel. Cover the pie tin with clear plastic wrap, and hold the plastic wrap in place with a rubber band or some tape.

2. Now pour some tomato soup into a glass. Cover the glass with plastic wrap and fasten it with tape or a rubber band.

3. Pour some tomato soup in another glass. This time rub your finger on the kitchen floor and poke it into the soup. Now seal the glass with plastic wrap, just like the other one, and mark it with an extra piece of tape so you'll remember which glass is which.

4. You'll need to have some patience for this step! Put all 3 containers in a quiet, dark place and check them whenever you want. In about a week you'll find something growing. What could it be? Try looking at it with a magnifying glass.

What Did You See?

Some fuzzy-looking plants grew in all the containers within a week. Unlike your sprouts, these plants did not look very pretty *or* good to eat—and they *aren't*. The food in the containers looked like it was rotting. You could see the plants better with a magnifying glass.

Why Did It Happen?

The tiny plants that grow in food are called molds. They grow from tiny, invisible spores, not from seeds like other plants do. Molds need only food, water, and air to grow. They can't produce their own food like other plants, so the soup you left out was its food. The mold grew faster in the soup with the dirt from the floor because the spores were already on the floor—and you put them right into the soup.

Advanced Activities

Spoon Flip

What can you do with a spoon besides eat?

Parent's Note:

Silverware has its typical uses, but this activity will stress how the physical design of spoons can be used for other purposes. (For example, the spoon can act as a lever to lift things.)

What You Need:

A plastic container; 2 plastic teaspoons (or soup spoons); plastic or masking tape; a plastic cup.

What To Do:

1. First, tape a plastic container to the kitchen counter. Now lay 2 teaspoons on the counter so the handle of the first spoon points toward the container and the handle of the second spoon lies under the bowl of the first spoon.

2. If you hit the bowl of the spoon farther away from the container with your fist, the spoon next to the container will flip up into the air. It might even land inside the container. Go ahead and try!

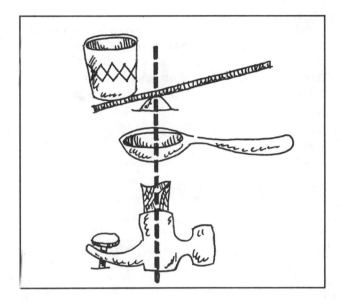

3. Keep practicing. How many times in a row can you flip the spoon into the container? Why do you think spoons can do this?

4. Now set a plastic cup on the end of the handle of a spoon. Slowly press down on the bowl of the spoon. What happens? How high can you lift the cup? Can you tip over the cup?

What Did You See?

When you hit one spoon with force, it flipped the other spoon into the air. Sometimes the other spoon landed in the container. You could lift the cup without even touching it.

Why Did It Happen?

The spoon acts like something called a lever. The spoon pivots, or turns, on the rounded bowl. This pivot point on a lever is called a *fulcrum*. Pushing the tip of the spoon down rocks the handle end up, knocking the second spoon into the air. The spoon works like a teeter-totter—when you push down the high end, the low end goes up. You can use a lever to lift things easily, just as you lifted the cup with the spoon.

Little Rafts

Can you make metal float?

Parent's Note:

In this activity you will help your child investigate another quality of water—the surface tension of water. Your child will learn how kitchen tap water can support (float) items that normally sink. Using a magnifying glass, your child will see how water swells up around the floating objects.

What You Need:

A large bowl; a fork; paper clips; a sewing needle; a wire screen; a magnifying glass.

What To Do:

1. You know that running water from the kitchen faucet can be very powerful. The force of the water can actually move things. I bet you didn't know that standing water is powerful, too. Let's see why. Fill a large bowl with ordinary kitchen water.

2. Place the large bowl on the kitchen counter. Put the paper clip in the water. What happens? Anything with holes in it should sink. Now lift the paper clip out of the water.

3. This time, place the paper clip on the tines of a fork. Lower the fork and paper clip gently onto the water. Remove the fork without touching the paper clip. Surprised?

4. Try floating other small metal items that would normally sink (e.g., a sewing needle, a tack, a nail, or a small screen with holes in it).

What Did You See?

When you dropped the paper clip into the water, it sank to the bottom of the bowl. But when you gently laid it onto the water with the fork, the paper clip floated. The water in the bowl bulged around the paper clip.

Why Did It Happen?

The tiny particles of water hold onto each other with a great deal of strength. When you drop something into the water, it breaks the water particles apart and sinks. But if you gently lay something flat on the water's surface, the water droplets act like rubber bands stretched between the object and the sides of the bowl. That's how some kinds of bugs can walk on water. Of course, if something is *too* heavy—like a bowling ball—water can't hold it up no matter *how* gently you lay it on the surface.

Run Away!

What happens when you mix soap and milk?

Parent's Note:

Children saw in the "Dirt Buster" activity how soap breaks up grease and holds the tiny droplets in suspension. This activity will show how soap weakens the ties between water droplets. We will use both water and milk to demonstrate the instant reaction between the soap and the water.

What You Need:

Milk; coffee grounds (or tea leaves); food coloring; liquid soap or detergent; a pie tin; a cookie sheet with edges or a large baking pan.

What To Do:

1. First, put some water in a pie tin and sprinkle some coffee grounds on top. See how evenly they float over the surface? Now put a drop of soap in the water. What happens?

2. Let's try the same thing with milk and food coloring. Pour enough milk to just cover the bottom of a large cookie sheet or pan. Now drop in a few big drops of food coloring. What do you think would happen if you dropped in some soap?

3. Try it! Drop 1 or 2 drops of soap into the middle of the drops of coloring. What happens? Does the milk act the same as the water? Try adding more soap. Do you think milk has water in it?

4. Now empty the cookie sheet, refill it, and add soap drops *away* from the food coloring drops. Any difference?

What Did You See?

The coffee grounds pulled away from the soap in the pan of water. The drops of coloring also pulled away from the soap in the pan of milk.

Why Did It Happen?

Tiny water droplets hold onto each other tightly—they even stretch when you pull them apart. Soap drops weaken the connections between water drops by clinging to them and pushing them apart. As the soap pushes some of the water drops apart, the rest of the water drops are crowded together in the space that's left in the bowl. Milk is mostly made of water, so it acts the same way water does.

Make It Shine

Can you make old, dirty pennies sparkle like new?

Parent's Note:

This activity will enable your children to test different combinations of common kitchen ingredients. Help them keep track of the various combinations by writing the names of the ingredients on small cards. Comparing the results of different combinations will provide a fun way for your children to learn about the scientific process.

What You Need:

5 small plastic bowls; 5 dark, dirty pennies; a tablespoon; teaspoons for stirring; salt; vinegar; liquid soap; a pencil; small cards or pieces of paper.

What To Do:

1. Let's try mixing some vinegar with some salt. Just pour 2 tablespoons of vinegar into a small bowl and add a teaspoon of salt. Does anything happen?

2. Now try adding a dirty penny to the vinegar and salt. It might look like nothing's happening, but give it some time.

3. While you're waiting, put 4 more old pennies into other common ingredients: put the first penny in a bowl of plain water; the second in a bowl of soap and water; the third in a bowl of plain vinegar; and the fourth in a bowl of plain salt. Have Mom or Dad help you put a card by each bowl listing what's inside.

4. Now sit back and wait! Check the pennies every 5 minutes or so. After 15 minutes, take all 5 pennies out and wipe them dry. What happened to them?

What Did You See?

The only bowl that cleaned the penny and made it look newer and shinier was the bowl with the vinegar and salt. Nothing else cleaned the penny—not even the bowl with water and soap!

Why Did It Happen?

What looks like dirt on the penny is actually *tarnish* caused by a chemical reaction between the copper the penny is made from and the air around it. Since tarnish isn't dirt, soap and water can't take it off. Instead, you need to use some weak acid that undoes the process that caused the tarnish. Using vinegar alone or salt alone will not work. Only when the salt and vinegar are combined do they form the acid that will remove the tarnish.

Stop the Leak

Can you poke holes in a bag without it leaking?

Parent's Note:

Children know that plastic bags can be useful. But one property of plastic bags that even most adults don't know is that they seal themselves around an object that punctures them. This simple experiment will demonstrate the self-sealing property of bags. Just be sure your children try this over the sink!

What You Need:

Plastic sandwich or vegetable bags; several long, sharp pencils.

What To Do:

1. First, fill a plastic bag at least half full with water and hold the top of the bag closed. Keep the bag over the sink.

2. What would happen if you stuck a sharp pencil right through the bag? Give it a try—but don't pull the pencil out once it's poked through! Does the bag leak?

3. What will happen if you pull the pencil out? Try it!

4. Can you put the pencil back in the same hole again? Does that stop the leak? Can you poke a second pencil through the bag, too?

What Did You See?

The bag did not leak water when you poked the pencil through the bag and left it there. But when you pulled the pencil out of the bag, the water drained out.

Why Did It Happen?

The type of plastic used to make bags is very stretchy and tends to close up around a tear. The pressure of the water in the bag wanting to get out also pushes the plastic tightly against the pencil. So both the stretchiness of the bag and the pressure of the water help to form a watertight seal around the pencil. When you pull the pencil out, the water runs out the little hole the pencil leaves behind.

Balancing Act

Can you balance a potato on the point of a toothpick?

Parent's Note:

Using forks to balance potatoes will be a new challenge for your children—something they probably never thought of before. Dinner forks stuck in the potato lower its center of gravity, making it easy to balance the potato on the tiny point of a toothpick.

What You Need:

Several raw potatoes; 2 dinner forks; some toothpicks; an unopened plastic bottle with a cap (a soft drink bottle works well).

What To Do:

1. First, let Mom or Dad help you cut a big piece of raw potato. Carefully stick a toothpick into the bottom of the potato—aim for the center!

2. Now try to balance the potato on top of a plastic bottle. Can you make it stand up on the toothpick?

3. Now stick 2 forks into the potato (as shown here) and try balancing it again. Be careful not to poke yourself with the sharp toothpick or the forks. You can move the forks to different positions to see if that helps.

4. Try balancing another potato that has a different shape or size. You can also try using just 1 fork or 3 forks.

What Did You See?

When the forks were stuck into the potato in just the right way, the potato balanced on the toothpick on top of the bottle.

Why Did It Happen?

The toothpick provides only a tiny little point for the potato to balance on—think how much harder it is for you to balance when you're standing tiptoe on one foot! The toothpick also raises something called the potato's *center of gravity*—the center point of the potato's weight. Things with a high center of gravity tip much more easily than things with a low center of gravity (that's why race cars are so low to the ground). The forks give the potato more weight and lower its center of gravity so it's more stable.

Egg Hunt

Can you tell if an egg is raw or cooked without cracking it?

Parent's Note:

The refrigerator offers children many lessons about science. You'll need to make some hard-boiled eggs for both this activity and the next one. Your children will finish this activity knowing much more about eggs—including how to tell a raw egg from a hard-boiled egg.

What You Need:

A few fresh and hard-boiled eggs; a bowl; a pencil; a magnifying glass (optional).

What To Do:

1. Do you think that eggshells have holes in them? How could you find out? Mark the pointed end of a raw egg with a pencil and put it in a bowl of warm water. Do you see bubbles coming from the egg? Where did they come from?

2. Take the egg out of the water and have Mom or Dad help you ca break it in half. Put the yolk an into a bowl. Look at the end of shell where the air bubbles ca What do you see inside? Could the air sac have seeped thr shell? Then the eggshell n holes!

3. Can you tell whether an egg is raw or hard-boiled without either breaking it open or marking it with a pen? Try spinning a raw egg and a hard-boiled egg on the kitchen counter. Notice any difference?

4. Which egg spins faster? longer? Break it open over a dish to see which egg it is!

What Did You See?

When you put a raw egg in water, bubbles came from anyplace in the egg, but most often from the round end. When you broke it open, you could see an air sac on the inside of the shell at the round end. The hard-boiled egg spun faster and longer than the raw egg.

Why Did It Happen?

Eggs have tiny holes in their shells. When you put an egg in water, air from its air sac escapes through these holes. A raw egg is more difficult to spin than a hard-boiled egg because the yolk and white inside a raw egg are liquid like water. When you spin a raw egg, the inside sloshes around in different directions, slowing down the spin. The hard-boiled egg spins faster because its yolk and white are solid, so everything in the egg travels in the same direction.

The Bouncing Egg

Can you remove an egg's shell without breaking it?

Parent's Note:

Eggs can teach children about lots of important—and fun—scientific information. This activity requires patience, but the final product is well worth the wait! Try another activity during the two days your children are waiting for results of this one.

What You Need:

A raw egg; a hard-boiled egg; vinegar; a plastic jar with a tight-fitting lid (or a clear plastic glass, plastic wrap, and a rubber band).

What To Do:

1. Start by putting an egg carefully in the jar and pouring enough vinegar in the jar to cover it. Close the lid tightly and put the jar on the kitchen counter. Check the jar several times a day to see what happens.

2. After two days, *carefully* remove the egg and wash it with cold water. What do you notice about it? You are holding the egg by a thin membrane, its covering inside the shell. Hold it up to the light, turn it, and look at it closely.

3. Hold the egg a few inches above the kitchen counter and drop it gently. Did it bounce a little? Try dropping it from different heights—but not too high. Then challenge your friends to bounce a raw egg without breaking it!

4. Try removing the shell from a hard-boiled egg the same way and then bouncing it.

What Did You See?

The shell was completely gone—you could even see the yolk and the white inside the raw egg. The egg bounced when you dropped it on the counter.

Why Did It Happen?

Vinegar is an acid, so it slowly dissolves the calcium that the eggshell is made of. Teeth and bones are made of calcium, and bacteria (plaque) on them dissolve your teeth and make cavities, which is why it is important to brush regularly! The hard-boiled egg also lost its shell and bounced—the only difference is that you can't see through it.

The Cannon

Can you make a homemade cannon?

Parent's Note:

Baking soda and vinegar are common, relatively safe, substances with all sorts of uses. Baking soda is a base, however, and vinegar is an acid, so when the two of them are mixed they react by bubbling like crazy! This activity will show how to use this reaction to generate a fun but very safe little explosion.

What You Need:

An empty, 16-ounce (or half-liter) soft drink bottle; a cork that fits the mouth of the bottle; vinegar; baking soda; a piece of paper towel 4 inches (or 10 centimeters) square; a ¼-cup measure; a tablespoon; a small funnel.

What To Do:

1. First, put 2 tablespoons of vinegar into a 1/4-cup (or 6-centiliters) measure. Hold the measuring cup over the sink and sprinkle a tablespoon of baking soda into the vinegar. What happens?

2. Next, take an empty soft drink bottle and fill it with ¼ cup (or 6-centiliters) of vinegar. Use a funnel—it helps!

3. Now pour a teaspoon of baking soda onto a small piece of paper towel, roll it up like a Tootsie roll, and drop the little bundle into the pop bottle.

4. Quickly wedge a wet cork just a little way into the mouth of the bottle, but not so far that you have to push it.

What Did You See?

When you mixed vinegar and baking soda together, they bubbled and fizzed. When you mixed them in the bottle, the fizzing popped the cork right out of the bottle. POW!

Why Did It Happen?

Vinegar and baking soda make bubbles when they're mixed. These bubbles are full of gas, and when the bubbles pop, they release thin gas into the air. When you seal vinegar and baking soda in a bottle, the gas from the bubbles builds up inside the bottle with no way to escape. The pressure from the gas increases until it finds the weakest point—the cork. Pop!

Kitchen Art

Can you create ornaments from flour?

Parent's Note:

Science in the kitchen is especially fun for children if they can make something that is pretty and lasting. This activity will show children how baking ingredients can be used for art as well as for food. If you want the ornaments to dry more quickly, put them in the oven at 250 degrees for 2 hours. The dried ornaments will last longer if painted with varnish, shellac, or liquid plastic.

What You Need:

Flour; salt; salad oil; food coloring; a mixing bowl; measuring cups and spoons; cookie cutters; a rolling pin; a cooling rack or cookie sheet; a table knife; a pencil.

What To Do:

1. First, measure 1 heaping cup of flour and 1/2 cup (or 1 deciliter) of salt into a mixing bowl. Stir them together with your fingers. It feels like sand!

2. Next, add 1/2 cup (or 1 deciliter) of water, colored with a few drops of your favorite food coloring, and a tablespoon of oil. Mix all the ingredients together with your fingers to make a ball of dough that feels like clay. Add more flour if the dough sticks to your fingers.

3. You can shape the dough into anything you want! Roll it out with a rolling pin and make ornament shapes with a table knife or cookie cutters. You can also shape it into animals or people. Use the point of a pencil to make holes in the ornaments so you can hang them later.

4. When you are done shaping the ornaments, place them on a cooling rack (it dries both sides evenly) and put the rack someplace to dry for a few days.

What Did You See?

When you mixed the ingredients, they stuck together to form a dough that acted like clay. The clay could be cut, rolled flat, and used to make shapes and ornaments. The ornaments dried and hardened in a few days (faster in the oven).

Why Did It Happen?

A common baking ingredient, flour, mixes with water to act like a glue to hold other ingredients together. Flour has special substances (proteins) that form *gluten*, a material that is very sticky when it is wet. When the dough dries out it becomes hard—almost as hard as a cup or a plate.

Order Form

Qty	Title	Author	Order #	Price	Total
	1,2,3...Play with me!	Pare, R.	2240	$12.95	
	A,B,C...Play with me!	Pare, R.	2230	$12.95	
	Baby & Child Medical Care	Hart, T.	1159	$7.95	
	Dads Say the Dumbest Things	Lansky/Jones	4220	$5.95	
	Dino Dots	Dixon, D.	2250	$4.95	
	Dictionary According to Mommy	Armor, J.	4110	$4.95	
	Discipline Without Shouting or Spanking	Wyckoff/Unell	1079	$5.95	
	Do They Ever Grow Up?	Johnston, L.	1089	$5.95	
	Free Stuff for Kids, 14th ed.	FS editors	2190	$4.95	
	It"s My Party!	Croasdale/Davis	2390	$5.95	
	Learn While You Scrub, Science in Tub	Lewis, J.	2350	$6.95	
	Mother Murphy's Law	Lansky, B.	1149	$4.50	
	Practical Parenting Tips	Lanksy, V.	1179	$6.95	
	Rub-a-Dub-Dub, Science in the Tub	Lewis, J.	2270	$5.95	
	Stork Didn't Bring Me	Hebert, M.	2220	$12.95	
				Subtotal	
				Shipping and Handling	
				MN residents add 6% sales tax	
				Total	

YES, please send me the books indicated above. Add $1.25 shipping and handling for the first book and $.50 for each additional book. Add $2.00 to total for books shipped to Canada. Overseas postage will be billed. Allow upto 4 weeks for delivery. Send check or money order payable to Meadowbrook Press. No cash or C.O.D.'s please. Quantity discounts available upon request. **Prices subject to change without notice.**

Send book(s) to:

Name _____

Address _____

City _____ **State** _____ **Zip** _____

_____ **Check enclosed for $** _____, payable to Meadowbrook Press

_____ **Charge to my credit card (for purchase of $10.00 or more)**

_____ **Phone orders call: (800) 338-2232 (for orders of $10.00 or more)**

Account # _____ **Visa** _____ **MasterCard** _____

Signature _____ **Expiration date** _____

Meadowbrook Press, 18318 Minnetonka Boulevard, Deephaven, MN 55391
(612) 473-5400 Toll Free (800) 338-2232